ROYAL OBSERVATORY GREENWICH

SOUVENIR GUIDE

D1404769

Contents

PREVIOUS PAGE: **The Royal Observatory** from the north, with a rainbow and, left, the 1930 statue of General James Wolfe (1727–59).

RIGHT: **The figure of Astronomy**, modelled by W.J. Neatby in 1895 as part of the Doulton terracotta decoration of the Observatory's South Building, completed in 1899.

Introduction

WELCOME TO THE ROYAL OBSERVATORY, GREENWICH, whose three linked themes are astronomy, time and navigation. Founded in 1675 to help produce an astronomical solution to the problem of finding one's longitude at sea, the Observatory came to define time and place for the world. Its history and the work done there explain why the International Prime Meridian – Longitude 000° 00' 00" – passes through Greenwich and why Greenwich Mean Time (GMT) is the basis of the time zone system.

This guide outlines the history of the Observatory's foundation and of the buildings on its ever-evolving site, and introduces the Astronomers Royal who lived and worked there for nearly three centuries. It explores the connection between practical astronomy, timekeeping and navigation at sea, and the changing work of the Observatory in its later history. All these themes are reflected in what you can see there today.

The Observatory opened to the public as part of the National Maritime Museum (NMM) in 1960. Since then, its domestic and working spaces have become galleries telling its own history, and of its role in the search for longitude and the histories of astronomy and timekeeping. It has also continued to inform the public about the work of modern astronomers, through the Weller Astronomy Galleries, workshops and classes for all ages, observing sessions and a variety of exciting shows in the Peter Harrison Planetarium.

In January 2012 the Observatory, Museum, Queen's House, and the *Cutty Sark*, were granted the title of Royal Museums Greenwich, marking HM The Queen's Diamond Jubilee. There are separate guides for each of them and all aspects of our activities at Greenwich are covered on our website, rmg.co.uk Enjoy your visit – and come again!

The Observatory from above the Greenwich Meridian (added in red), looking south.

Origins: the Longitude Problem

THE FOUNDATION OF THE ROYAL OBSERVATORY was one of a number of initiatives across Europe in response to 'the longitude problem'. The ability to determine accurate longitude, or east–west position, at sea was becoming an ever-more pressing need, as merchants, companies and nations competed for dominance of international trading opportunities. While navigators could make reasonably accurate measurements of latitude (north–south position), using the angle of the Sun or stars above the horizon, no simple reference points existed for longitude.

It was understood since Classical times that difference in longitude is relative to the difference in time between two places. Put simply, if the circumference of the Earth is divided into 360 degrees, every hour difference in local time between two places equals 15 degrees of longitude ($360° \div 24\,\text{hrs} = 15°$). However, while it was possible to measure local time at sea by the Sun or stars, there was no means of knowing the time at another reference point. Even by the seventeenth century, no clock or watch was capable of keeping accurate time over a long voyage on a moving ship.

The ancient Greeks recognized that astronomy might provide a solution. If a lunar eclipse, for example, could be viewed simultaneously from two places, a record of the exact *local* time the event occurred in each place would show their difference in longitude. Lunar eclipses were too rare for navigational purposes but the idea that the position of the Moon relative to the background of stars might act as a celestial clock existed from at least the early sixteenth century. However, making such an idea workable required the accumulation of a huge amount of astronomical data.

A Dutch merchant ship running between rocks in rough weather, by Willem van de Velde, the Younger, 1651. The safety, reliability and profits of maritime trade generated interest in navigational science. BHC0911

Royal Interest

ASTRONOMICAL INFORMATION of sufficient quantity and accuracy to aid navigation, cartography and timekeeping required new observatories. Interest in solving the longitude problem led to the foundation of the Paris Observatory in 1667 and the Royal Observatory at Greenwich in 1675. In both cases the ruling monarch was convinced that national interests were at stake and justified this investment in science.

In Britain, Charles II apparently learned about the potential importance of astronomy to his navy and his kingdom's prosperity from his French mistress, Louise de Kéroualle, Duchess of Portsmouth. She is said to have told the King about a proposal from a Frenchman called Le Sieur de St Pierre. His idea was that creating tables that predicted the position of the Moon from two places at once would make it possible to work out the difference in local time between the two places and therefore longitude. Charles was sufficiently persuaded to appoint a Royal Commission to examine the matter.

The Commissioners included fellows of the Royal Society of London, some of whom had already been looking for support to found an observatory for the Society. Two of these fellows were Sir Christopher Wren, the King's Surveyor-General and formerly professor of astronomy at Oxford, and Robert Hooke, curator to the Royal Society and professor of geometry at Gresham College. With Sir Jonas Moore, a mathematician and Surveyor-General of the Ordnance, and his protégé, a young astronomer called John Flamsteed, they reported that St Pierre's method might, indeed, work in theory, but that the foundation of an observatory and the appointment of an astronomer to accumulate the necessary data would be essential to make any astronomical solution a reality.

OPPOSITE AND DETAIL LEFT:
Charles II, *c.*1670, after Sir Peter Lely. Charles never visited his Observatory but his interest in what science could do for the nation led to its foundation. BHC2609

OVERLEAF: **The Royal Observatory** from Croom's Hill, *c.*1696. This shows Flamsteed House, with the Queen's House below. Behind it are a 60-foot telescope, Flamsteed's meridian observatory and the outhouse over his well telescope. BHC1812

John Flamſteed A. R.
F.R.S.

Foundation of the Observatory

O N 4 MARCH 1675, the Royal Commission reported back to Charles II, recommending the foundation of an observatory and the appointment of an astronomer. His response, according to Flamsteed's later account, was to call for immediate action. The work, he said, 'must be carried out in royal fashion' for he 'did not want his ship-owners and sailors to be deprived of any help the Heavens could supply.'

The same day, Charles issued a royal warrant that named Flamsteed his 'astronomical observator', appointed to 'apply himself with the most exact Care and Diligence to the rectifying of the Tables of the Motions of the Heavens, and the places of the fixed Stars, so as to find out the so much desired Longitude of Places for the perfecting of the art of Navigation.' Shortly afterwards, Sir Christopher Wren was charged with designing an observatory, and Sir Jonas Moore with constructing and equipping it.

Various sites were considered but Wren's suggestion of using that of ruined Greenwich Castle was quickly taken up. Its merits included solid foundations that could be reused and its location in a royal park, on high ground, away from London's smoke but accessible by river or road. Wren presumably oversaw the design but the 'laying out' of the building, and other work, was left to his assistant, Robert Hooke, who also made some of the Observatory's instruments. Just £500 was allocated to the project. The funds came from the sale of spoilt gunpowder for reprocessing and costs were also saved by using 'recycled' building materials. The final four per cent overspend to only £520 9s 1d (£520.45) was an achievement modern projects might envy.

The foundation stone was laid on 10 August 1675 and Flamsteed was installed by 10 July 1676. Regular work with his new clocks and instruments began that autumn, signalling the start of a new era for Greenwich and for astronomy, time and navigation.

OPPOSITE: **John Flamsteed**, aged 35. A portrait by Thomas Murray, 1684, in the collection of the Royal Society, London.

BELOW: **Greenwich Castle**, from a print of 1637 by Wenceslaus Hollar. Originally a 15th-century hunting lodge, later improved as a 'grace-and-favour' royal residence, it was in ruins by the time Wren suggested it as a site for the Observatory. PAJ2421

The Astronomers Royal and their Assistants

JOHN FLAMSTEED (1646–1719) was the first Astronomer Royal to live and work at the Observatory in Greenwich. He held the post for a remarkable 42 years, completing tens of thousands of observations. These were ultimately, and posthumously, published in a catalogue, *Historia Coelestis Britannica* (1725), and a star atlas, *Atlas Coelestis* (1729). After Flamsteed, there were another nine Astronomers Royal based at Greenwich, each charged with making observations to improve astronomy and navigation:

Edmond Halley (1656–1742)	AR 1720–42
James Bradley (1692–1762)	AR 1742–62
Nathaniel Bliss (1700–64)	AR 1762–64
Nevil Maskelyne (1732–1811)	AR 1765–1811
John Pond (1767–1836)	AR 1811–35
Sir George Biddell Airy (1801–92)	AR 1835–81
Sir William Christie (1845–1922)	AR 1881–1910
Sir Frank Dyson (1868–1939)	AR 1910–33
Sir Harold Spencer Jones (1890–1960)	AR 1933–55

Although the Astronomers Royal were appointed by the monarch, they had little direct contact with the court. Rather, from 1710, they were subject to the scrutiny and advice of a Board of Visitors, made up of the President and members of the Council of the Royal Society. Initially financed by the Board of Ordnance, the Observatory was never generously funded, although it steadily expanded after transfer to the Admiralty in 1818.

This expansion is particularly noticeable when considering the number of astronomical assistants available to help with observation and calculations. In the seventeenth and eighteenth centuries there was usually only one such assistant, who lived within the Observatory and often endured a monotonous and lonely existence. In the nineteenth century the workforce expanded significantly and by the end of the century there were some sixty members of staff, with only the Astronomer Royal, his family and domestic servants living on-site.

ABOVE: **George Biddell Airy** (detail), by John Collier, 1883. BHC2507

OPPOSITE CLOCKWISE FROM TOP LEFT:
Four Astronomers Royal: Edmond Halley (by Kneller, BHC2734), Nathaniel Bliss (unknown artist, BHC4144), William Christie (B0718) and Harold Spencer Jones (B0953).

The Work of the Observatory

T HE MOST SIGNIFICANT WORK of the astronomers at Greenwich was the series of fundamental observations made with telescopes aligned on a meridian (a line between the North and South Poles). This mounting allows accurate and repeated observations of heavenly bodies as they appear to revolve around the celestial pole over the course of the night. The Sun, Moon and planets can likewise be observed as they 'cross' the instrument's meridian.

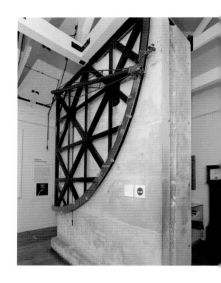

It was the job of the astronomer and his assistant to take measurements of the angular height (or declination) of the star above the celestial equator at the moment it crossed. By noting the exact time of this transit they could also calculate the other necessary co-ordinate, known as right ascension. A series of mathematical calculations would then 'reduce' these basic observations into a form that could be tabulated or mapped and thereby become useful to others.

Although the Royal Observatory was Britain's first state-funded scientific institution, for nearly a century its meridian observations were only published occasionally. The Astronomers Royal might announce new findings and they frequently supplied data privately within the scientific community, but it was only in the 1760s that annual publication became a requirement.

In the nineteenth and twentieth centuries, meridian observations remained central to the Observatory's work and international reputation, aiding navigation, cartography and timekeeping. Its tasks also expanded to include various services for the Navy and nation, and new techniques in the physical sciences. There was also increasing support for less utilitarian work, although the strength of the Observatory was always the production of long series of accurate data rather than new discoveries.

OPPOSITE TOP:
George Graham's 8-foot mural quadrant, made for Edmond Halley, 2nd Astronomer Royal, in 1725. It is mounted on the original 1720s meridian wall. AST0970

OPPOSITE BOTTOM:
Edward Troughton's 10-foot transit telescope. Made in 1816 for the Royal Observatory, this is displayed in its original location, on Bradley's Greenwich meridian of 1750. AST0982

RIGHT: **The Airy Transit Circle** at Greenwich, as shown in E. Dunkin's, *The Midnight Sky* (1891). This instrument of 1851, designed by George Airy, 7th Astronomer Royal, combined a transit telescope with a mural circle. F5926

Home and Work

A<small>S</small> S<small>IR</small> C<small>HRISTOPHER</small> W<small>REN</small> later recalled, the building soon known as Flamsteed House was built 'for the Observator's habitation & a little for Pompe'. It provided a fairly modest dwelling for the astronomer and his household in its ground floor and basement. 'Pompe' was provided by the first floor's high-windowed Star Chamber (now the Octagon Room) and the façade presented towards the Queen's House below.

Flamsteed used this chamber for entertaining distinguished visitors and some observations, although these were largely abandoned there in later years. Because the building had reused the foundations of Greenwich Castle, its alignment was not suited to meridian observations. For this reason there was an outbuilding in the south-east corner of the original courtyard that contained a meridian wall (aligned exactly north–south) and the most

BELOW: **Plan of the Royal Observatory, Greenwich**, engraved by Francis Place c.1676, showing Flamsteed House, the rear courtyard and original meridian observatory (M and O). B1652-16A

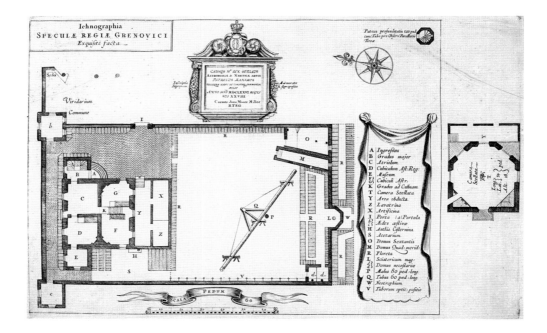

ABOVE: **Flamsteed House**, clearly showing the rear extension (left), added in the 1830s to provide additional living space for the large Airy family.

OVERLEAF: **View of the Royal Observatory** from the south-east, c.1770. The perspective is skewed, but the 1750 meridian building is on the right, before Airy extended it further from 1850 onwards. AST0042

important instruments. Despite the impressive number and accuracy of the observations that Flamsteed made in this small observatory, it proved structurally unstable and his successors began a series of new meridian buildings to the east, away from the slope of the hill. These were enlarged several times as new and better instruments were successively introduced. Today, these instruments have been remounted in their original locations, providing a timeline of the eighteenth- and nineteenth-century working observatory.

Flamsteed House was also extended several times, reflecting the rising status and different requirements of successive Astronomers Royal. Significant additions were made on the appointments of George Airy, in 1835, and Frank Dyson, in 1910, to provide accommodation for their large families. Over two-and-a-half centuries, the Royal Observatory was home to many children, servants, cooks and nursemaids, as well as astronomers.

The 18th-century Quest for Longitude

As WILLIAM MAITLAND WROTE in the mid-eighteenth century, 'Navigation is of so great Consequence to Mankind in general, that any Attempt to improve it is certainly in itself laudable'. By that time mariners had a range of instruments for plotting their course and position, and these were successfully used by many ships along established trading routes. Apart from the compass they included the backstaff and then the octant, with which navigators could fairly accurately determine their latitude, or north–south position.

Nonetheless, improvements were always being sought. Seamen knew that existing methods of position-finding were prone to error, sometimes with disastrous results, and they still needed a way of accurately determining their east–west position or longitude. This was extremely difficult at sea, above all because of the motion of the ship. Countries including Spain had already unsuccessfully offered prizes for solutions to the longitude problem but in 1714 the British government tried the same approach. The Longitude Act of that year offered rewards of up to £20,000 (worth several millions today) for successful methods of finding longitude at sea, and established a group of Commissioners to assess the proposals.

For decades many sought these rewards, but it was only in the 1760s that two practicable methods came to fruition and began to be proved at sea, most famously on the circumnavigations of Captain James Cook. One used a timekeeper, the other used astronomical means, but both relied on the fact that the longitudinal distance between two places can be calculated by knowing the local time at each. Over time both methods became commonly used.

ABOVE: **Backstaff** by Will Garner, 1734. Backstaves were developed in the seventeenth century for determining latitude from the Sun's position. Their use continued for much of the eighteenth century. NAV0041

RIGHT: **Octant** by George Adams, 1753. Developed for measuring the positions of the Moon, Sun and stars, octants continued in use throughout the nineteenth century. NAV1282

RIGHT: **Azimuth compass** invented by Ralph Walker, c.1793. Walker's compass received a reward from the Commissioners for Longitude. Although Walker believed it could be used for determining longitude, the reward was given because it was considered a good compass, something that was always essential for navigation. NAV0263

OVERLEAF:**The Royal Observatory** from the north, in a snowbound winter setting.

BELOW: **The Observatory** from the east, *c*.1840, including chimneys later removed from the rear extension, the dome of St Paul's in the far distance and one of the windmills at Millwall, lower right. PAD8920

Astronomy and Longitude

To DETERMINE A SHIP'S LONGITUDE from the Moon and stars – the 'lunar-distance' method – you need to know exactly where they are meant to be. In other words, you need accurate tables of their predicted positions for the entire length of your voyage, which might last one or more years in some cases.

The Royal Observatory at Greenwich was one of several European observatories founded to produce the astronomical data navigators needed. This meant that it had to have the best astronomical instruments, in order to map the positions of the stars and other celestial bodies very accurately. This work also relied on observers and human 'computers' to carry out the observations and do the complex calculations to turn these into usable data.

At Greenwich, it was the Astronomer Royal who oversaw all of this work. Nevil Maskelyne (1732–1811), fifth Astronomer Royal from 1765, had a particularly important role in bringing astronomical methods of longitude determination into use at sea. Having been one of a number of people who had tested methods on ocean voyages, as Astronomer Royal he instigated and took responsibility for producing the *Nautical Almanac*, the tables for astronomical navigation, published annually from 1767. The techniques he promoted came into more widespread use in the nineteenth century, when new ways of using the stars for navigation also began to be developed.

ABOVE:

Drawing for a cameo brooch commemorating Nevil Maskelyne. He is shown with the Moon in the background and a quote from Ovid's *Heroides*, both alluding to his role in promoting astronomical methods of navigation. L4505

Navigating by the Stars

ALL NAVIGATION AT SEA needs instruments that can make accurate observations from a moving ship. Chief among these was the marine sextant, which was developed in the late 1750s during trials of astronomical methods of navigation. The sextant (one sixth of a circle) is a development of the octant (an eighth), its longer scale being better suited to measuring angular distances between the Moon and stars for longitude calculation.

With improved manufacturing processes, in particular through the invention of the dividing engine by the London instrument maker, Jesse Ramsden (1735–1800), sextants and octants became smaller, easier to handle and more accurate. As a result, they would become a standard tool of navigation – and of other practices such as surveying and hydrography – for the next 200 years.

However, the rise of navigational methods using astronomy and time-keepers did not spell the end of older methods that used the compass, the continuous monitoring of the speed of the ship, and other information such as the depth of water. These were still needed day-to-day and were indispensable when clouds obscured the sky. Continuous effort went into improving long-used instruments such as the magnetic compass, and into developing new ones for measuring depth and speed.

ABOVE: **Sextant** by John Bird, *c.*1758. One of the earliest surviving sextants. The large size meant that this instrument required a supporting pole to make handling easier. Sextants are one sixth of a circle; octants, an eighth. NAV1177

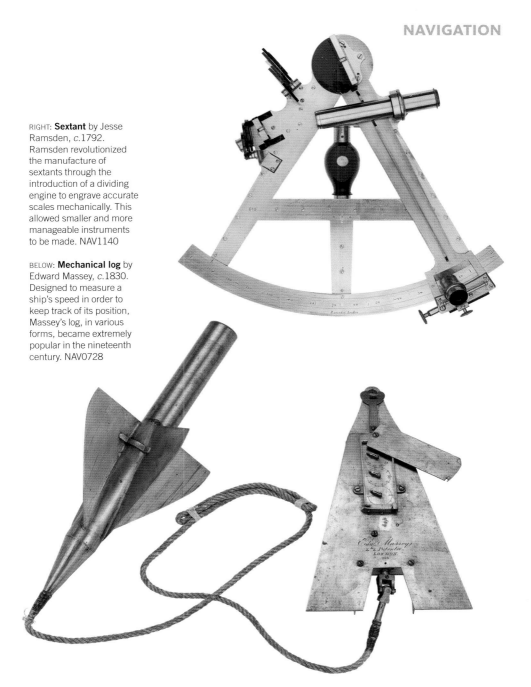

RIGHT: **Sextant** by Jesse Ramsden, *c.*1792. Ramsden revolutionized the manufacture of sextants through the introduction of a dividing engine to engrave accurate scales mechanically. This allowed smaller and more manageable instruments to be made. NAV1140

BELOW: **Mechanical log** by Edward Massey, *c.*1830. Designed to measure a ship's speed in order to keep track of its position, Massey's log, in various forms, became extremely popular in the nineteenth century. NAV0728

Longitude by Timekeeper

AS ALREADY EXPLAINED, measuring longitude at sea is a matter of knowing the time where you are and the time at a known starting point. The difference gives relative east–west position at the rate of 1° of longitude for every four minutes of time. The Sun can provide local time by observation at around noon each day. 'Home time', where you started, can also be found by astronomy; but it can only be kept – for easy, regular reference – by having a clock set to it. Such a clock must be one that will keep going, with high accuracy, under all conditions found in a moving ship at sea.

RIGHT: **Marine timekeeper 'C'** by Henry Sully, 1724. The poor performance of Sully's timekeepers seemed to confirm that the concept of a marine timekeeper was not practical. ZBA2248

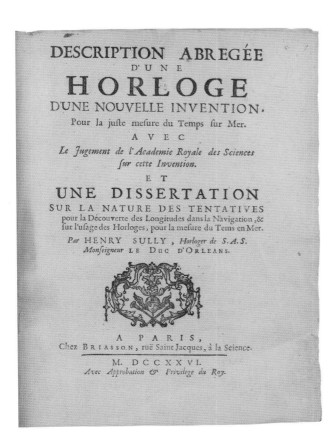

DESCRIPTION ABREGÉE
D'UNE
HORLOGE
D'UNE NOUVELLE INVENTION.
Pour la juste mesure du Temps sur Mer.
AVEC
Le Jugement de l'Académie Royale des Sciences sur cette Invention.
ET
UNE DISSERTATION
SUR LA NATURE DES TENTATIVES
pour la Découverte des Longitudes dans la Navigation, & sur l'usage des Horloges, pour la mesure du Tems en Mer.

Par HENRY SULLY, Horloger de S.A.S. Monseigneur LE DUC D'ORLEANS.

A PARIS,
Chez BRIASSON, rue Saint Jacques, à la Science.
M. DCCXXVI.
Avec Approbation & Privilege du Roy.

BELOW: **Sully's clock**, as illustrated in his book, with a table clock, chart and other instruments.

ABOVE: **'Short description of a newly invented clock...'.** The title page of the book Sully published on his invention in 1724. PBD6076

Until the mid-1600s clocks were too inaccurate to be used in this way. In the 1650s, however, clocks controlled by a pendulum were invented, which were capable of keeping time to within a few seconds a day. Several attempts were made to create a workable marine timekeeper using them but (almost needless to say) pendulums do not work well on a rocking ship and all these failed.

Henry Sully, an English clockmaker who worked mostly in Paris in the 1720s, attempted an improved version of one of these clocks. His design had a swinging balance wheel instead of a pendulum but it also failed, causing him bitter disappointment.

John Harrison, 1693–1776

HARRISON, a joiner and clockmaker from Lincolnshire, was one of many 'hopefuls' inspired by the great longitude prizes offered by the British government in 1714.

In the mid-1720s he began designing precision clocks and, after seeking advice from scientific contacts in London, built his first marine timekeeper, known today as H1, between 1730 and 1735. Encouraged by its good performance on a semi-official trial to Lisbon in 1736, members of the Board of Longitude awarded Harrison considerable sums of money over the next twenty years to develop two further large timekeepers (H2 and H3). However, by the mid-1750s Harrison realized he had taken the wrong course and quietly started work on a much smaller design. This resulted in H4, his celebrated fourth marine timekeeper of 1759, which took the form of a large watch. When officially tested, twice, on voyages to the West Indies, H4 performed extraordinarily well.

ABOVE: **John Harrison**, depicted in a print of 1768, after a portrait by Thomas King, with his large H3 timekeeper in the background and H4 lying on the table, left. PAG6373

It proved to be not only a workable solution to the longitude problem but was also the very first of all precision watches. A copy made in 1769 by the top London watchmaker, Larcum Kendall, was tested by Captain James Cook on his second and third Pacific voyages, and convinced him that it was a practical solution.

While a successful prototype, H4 was very complicated and expensive to reproduce. It was chiefly the work of two other London watchmakers, John Arnold and Thomas Earnshaw, which saw Harrison's design developed into the 'modern' marine chronometer, which went on to serve the navies of the world for the next one-and-a-half centuries.

BELOW: **Harrison's fourth marine timekeeper, H4**, the first precision watch and considered by many today as the most important timekeeper ever constructed. ZAA0037

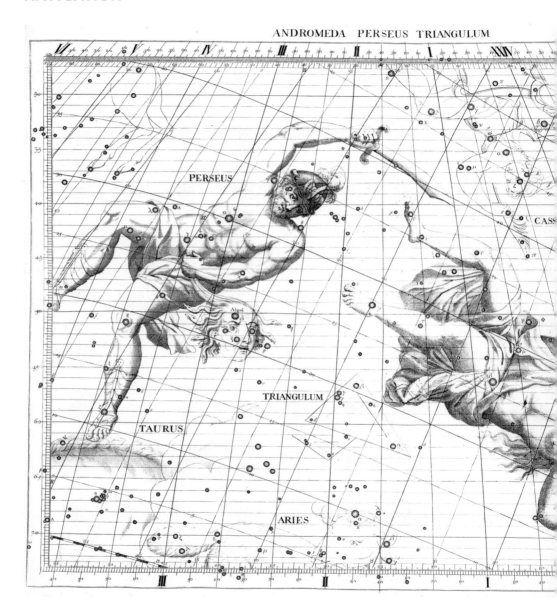

ANDROMEDA PERSEUS TRIANGULUM

PERSEUS

Algol

TRIANGULUM

TAURUS

ARIES

CASS

Mapping Scientific Knowledge

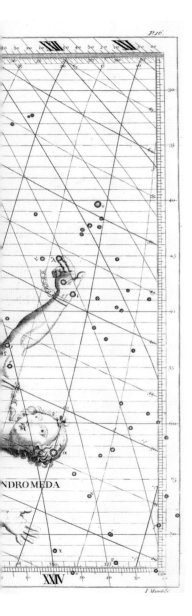

As NEW DISCOVERIES were made about astronomy, geophysics and oceanography, all were plotted on maps and charts of differing sorts, so that they could be analysed and made public. Using the most accurate timekeepers, John Flamsteed, the first Astronomer Royal, set out to record the positions of the stars relative to the Greenwich meridian as they crossed it each night. The resulting catalogues enabled him to create accurate charts of the heavens. He was reluctant to publish his results prematurely but prepared the contents for a great atlas of the stars, which appeared after his death. The star maps in the atlas were decorated with symbols of the constellations drawn by James Thornhill, who was the artist of the Painted Hall at Greenwich.

Edmond Halley, who became the second Astronomer Royal, travelled to St Helena to plot the stars visible from the southern hemisphere. He also undertook two ocean voyages, sponsored by the Admiralty, to measure terrestrial magnetism and to settle the question of whether patterns in magnetic variation – the difference between magnetic north and true north across the surface of the globe – could be of any use in determining longitude. He drew lines joining points of equal magnetic value and thus created the first isogonic chart. Halley also mapped the direction and strength of the trade winds and the tides, as well as predicting the timing and the path across Britain that the solar eclipse of 1715 would take. The focus of Halley's work at the Royal Observatory was on the motion of the Moon.

LEFT: **Andromeda, Perseus and Triangulum**, three constellations on a sheet from John Flamsteed's *Atlas Coelestis*, 1729. This vast star atlas contained the results of years of careful astronomical observation. PBN0237

OVERLEAF: **Edmond Halley's 'A new and correct sea chart of the whole world…'.** Published in 1701 this chart, showing world magnetic variation in 1700, plots the results of the first British state-sponsored scientific expedition with the aim of improving the safety of navigation. G201:1/1A-B

NORWAY Stockholm

RUSSIA
OR
MUSCOVY

Ad

IlleGigan

Qui Jov

Assyrio q

Oppos

Pellæo frus

Roman

Latius at

Cærula

ANNA maris

Auxilia

SCOTLAND
THE German
OCEAN
SWEDEN
LIFLAND
COURLAND

IRELAND
ENGLAND
London
HOLLAND
Amsterdam
POLAND

FLANDERS
GERMANY
HUNGARY
VKRAIN
CRIM TARTARS
Astracan

FRANCE
VENICE
ITALY
GULF OF VENICE
BULGARIA
BLACK SEA
GEOR
CASPIAN
SEA
14

SPAIN
PORTUGAL
SARDINIA
Sicily
GREECE
ANATOLIA
ARMENIA
MEDIA

MEDITERRANEAN SEA
TURKISH

BARBARY
REG FEZ
R. TUNIS
TRIPOLI
R. TRIPOLI
MARMARICA
EGYPT
EMPIRE
SYRIA
Aleppo
Antiochia
Jerusalem
AEMPIRE
PERSIA

REG MAROCO
ARABIA PETRÆA
Medina
Meca
ARABIA DESERTA
Ormus

GUALATA

ARGUIN
GUINEA

ARABIA
FELIX

To his Royall Highness
Prince GEORGE of DENMARK
LORD HIGH ADMIRALL of ENGLAND
Generalissimo of all her Maᵗⁱᵉˢ Forces &ᶜ
This Chart is humbly Dedicated
by his Highness most Obedient Serᵗ
Edmond Halley.

I. Harris Sculp.

Gold Coast
BINNI
BIAFARA

THE RED SEA
STREIG of BABELMANDEL
Costa d'Abassin
Costa
Barbara
MAGADOXA

INDIAN

GABON
AFRICA
LOANGO
CONGO
INTERIORA
ANGOLA
QUILOA
MOZAMBIQUE
Incognita
MATAMAN
MONO
CIMBEBAS
MOTA
ZOFALA
Comoro Isles
SEA
15

MADAGASCAR
OR
ST LAURENCE

Ascension

S. Helena

Monte
Negro

EASTERN

TARTARY

The Coast and Seas between Japon Corea
and Yedso are hitherto undiscovered
and it is not known whether
Yedso bea part of the Continent
or not

YEDSO

S. James
C. Patience
Robben I.
Salmon
Bay
C. Aniwa
Portland
Staten
Island
C. Anael
Ceroen

Comp
Lar

North Cape

LE OTUNG
Peking
EMPIRE
ZANTUM
OF
NANKING
CHINA

Bay
of
Nanquin
Flavius
Croceus
Kiang
Nanking

Vedo
Surrunaga
Meaco
Osaca

JAPO

TONSA
CICOKO

Firan
Langoxima
Nangai

Lesso
I. Summa

Tanaxima

I. de Liampo
I. Chouson
Liampo
Sumbar

CHEKIANG

Fucho
los Hermanes

Deserta
Duas Colunas
Una Coluna

FOCHI
CANTON

HIEU

Amsterdam

I dos Reys
Magos

Canton
Macao

Toan

FORMOSA

East Variation

TUNKING

BAY
OF
TUNKING
COCHINCHINA

HAINAN I.

Buches

Bavador

C. d'Engano
C. Boiac

PHILIPINE
ILUCON

Pracel

LADRON
ISLES

Pagan
Gregan
Haban

I. Guersa

los Herne

SIAM
Siam

Martaman

Chumu

Mindora

Streight of Manila
IS.
St. Sant

I. Juana

PEGU

ARACAN

GOLCONDA
Surat

INDOSTAN

BENGALA
R. Ganges

BAY
OF
BENGALL

SIAM

BAY
OF
SIAM

CAMBODIA

Mindanoa

I. S. John
I. Matelotes
I. S. John

I. Vincent

I. S. Bernduos

I. Pacas
I. de Alonso

La Martircos

I. dos Saltaodores

Mira como

Ilocan

MOLUCCA ISLES

GILOLO

Schowten I.
I. Moa
Burning hill

NOVA
BRITANIA

BORNEO

Succadana

CELEBES

TERRA DE PAPOS NOVA GUINEA

Dampeirs Streight

JAVA

STREIGHTS

HOLLANDIA

Arnheem
Land

Vanderlin

A. Tasman R.
Maatsuyker
River

R. Caron

Batavia R.
Caen R.

Elsse C.

Sea Charts and Land Maps

KING CHARLES II set up the Observatory at Greenwich to improve the safety of seafaring. Most sea charts produced in Britain in the late seventeenth century were graduated for latitude but not for longitude. The chart of the Isles of Scilly surveyed in 1683 by Greenville Collins lacked both: it was there that Sir Cloudesley Shovell's fleet was wrecked with great loss of life in 1707.

From the 1760s, with the introduction of Nevil Maskelyne's tables for finding longitude at sea by astronomical means, and Harrison's timekeepers for doing so that way, charting of the whole world took on new scientific accuracy. As astronomical tables were based on Greenwich, charts were too. Captain Cook charted the Endeavour River in Australia as 214° 42' 30" west of Greenwich, an error of only two-and-a-half minutes of arc.

The mapping of Britain by the Ordnance Survey is also based on the prime meridian at Greenwich but, because the Survey began in 1791, the meridian used was that defined in 1750 by James Bradley, third Astronomer Royal. While the Survey is still based on Bradley's meridian, in 1851 Britain's prime meridian (and later the world's) became that set by George Airy's new transit telescope about six metres to the east. The distance between them is roughly three-tenths of a second of arc, an insignificant amount for practical purposes at the time.

Airy, seventh Astronomer Royal, compiled the co-ordinates of a vast number of places, with their longitude expressed in relation to his new prime meridian at Greenwich. By then the invention of the electric telegraph, and its use to transmit time measurements, made it possible to locate distant points and foreign observatories with great precision.

LEFT: **Lord Boyne and friends** in the cabin of his yacht, plotting their course from Venice to Lisbon using sea charts and a crown compass, which is suspended from the deck-head. Oil painting after Bartolommeo Nazari, *c.*1732. BHC2567

OVERLEAF: **Part of a southern hemisphere star chart** from Reiner Ottens's *Atlas Maior* (1730), with the Greenwich Observatory (left) and the Round Tower observatory in Copenhagen (right). D4698

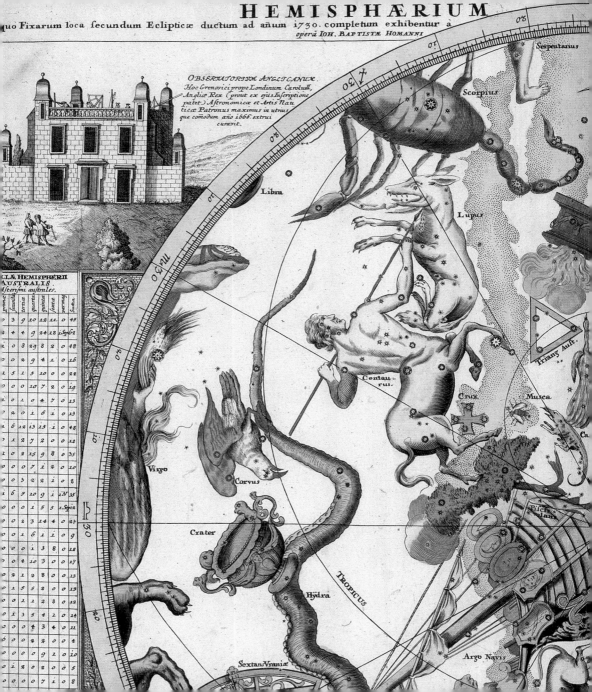

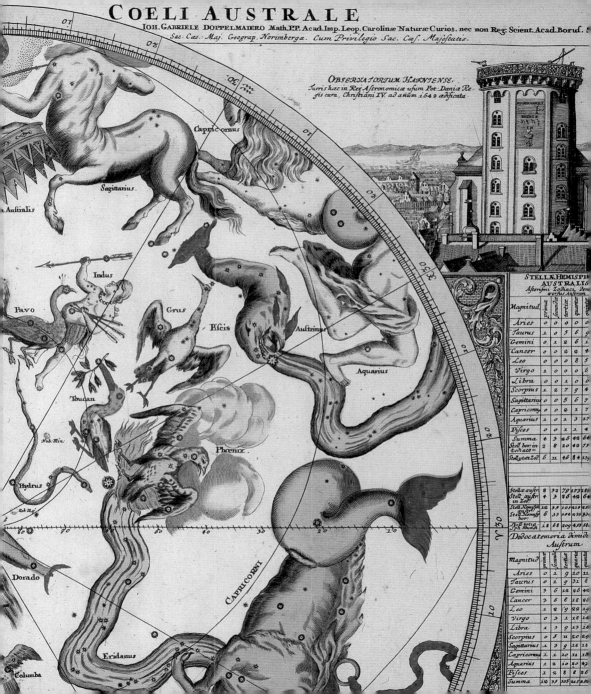

Time for the Observatory: Flamsteed and Tompion

ASTRONOMY AND TIME are inextricably linked. Our view of the heavens is governed by the Earth's angular rotation, which also gives us day and night, and our concept of time measurement.

The first Astronomer Royal, John Flamsteed, began making observations from the Queen's House while the Observatory was being built atop the hill in Greenwich Park. He moved there in July 1676 and, in order to create a catalogue of the 'fixed' stars, first needed to be sure that Earth's speed of rotation was constant.

BELOW: **'The Star Room'**, or Octagon Room, *c.*1712, shown in a print by Francis Place. ZBA1808

While astronomers had previously assumed this was the case, lives would depend on Flamsteed's star mapping and so it could not be based on an unproven assumption. In order to establish his work (and that of subsequent Astronomers Royal) on a firm footing, he needed accurate timekeeping. His patron, Sir Jonas Moore, therefore commissioned two extraordinary year-going clocks, which were installed in the panelling of the Star Room (today's Octagon Room). They were ordered from Thomas Tompion, then London's leading clock, watch

and scientific instrument maker. The clocks had 14-foot pendulums, which were driven by a new type of escapement devised by Flamsteed's friend and fellow astronomer, the mathematician Richard Townley.

Although not very accurate by today's standards, these were state-of-the-art timekeepers in the 1670s and sufficiently reliable for Flamsteed to conclude that the Earth's motion was indeed constant. In meridian-observation work the relationship between clock and telescope is symbiotic: the transit of the Sun, Moon or of a star is observed and timed by the clock and, in turn, the clock's rate is checked by observations.

OPPOSITE: **The Octagon Room today**. The north end looks much the same as in Place's print (above). This view looks the other way, with one of Tompion's original Observatory clocks on the right, converted long ago to 'grandfather' form.

Progressing Precision

WHEN EDMOND HALLEY moved in as second Astronomer Royal in 1721, the Observatory had been stripped of instruments. Flamsteed's widow had successfully claimed ownership of the clocks and telescopes and sold them all. Halley was granted £500 to re-equip and called upon Thomas Tompion's successor in business, George Graham, to make him a quadrant and an astronomical clock. Not only was Graham a talented watch, clock and instrument maker but, importantly, he was also a well respected astronomer. Graham's understanding of the weaknesses of contemporary instruments enabled him to produce examples of unparalleled quality, and his designs were copied by many other makers for years to come. Graham supplied three long-case regulator clocks to the Observatory. The third, known as Graham No. 3, came in 1750, and had an extraordinary working life of 174 years.

The success of the design was due to the high-quality mechanics, the dead-beat escapement (Graham's development of an earlier design by Tompion, his former master) and the temperature-compensated pendulum. The basic regulator introduced by Graham in the 1720s was not improved until the early 1800s, when William Hardy supplied a particularly fine one with a new escapement design to John Pond, the sixth Astronomer Royal.

The nineteenth century saw rapid development in Observatory timekeeping. The introduction of electrical systems enabled the staff to make ever-more accurate observations and advance some way towards eliminating the problem of the 'personal equation' – the varying reaction times of different observers.

William Hamilton Shortt's free-pendulum clock system was first used as the sidereal ('star-time') standard at the Observatory in 1925 and its accuracy facilitated the discovery that the Earth's speed of rotation was not exactly constant after all.

Troughton's transit telescope (see pp.18–19) set up on Bradley's Greenwich meridian of 1750. Also pictured are a Graham's No. 3 regulator (1750, right) and a Hardy regulator of his 1810 design (centre). ZBA0709, ZAA0606

Time for the Navy: the Marine Chronometer

U P UNTIL THE EARLY 1800s the Royal Navy preferred to use both marine chronometers and 'lunar distances', the alternative astronomical technique, for finding longitude at sea. Both were supported by 'dead-reckoning', the traditional means of estimating position by course speed, time and distance. By the 1830s, however, the Naval establishment finally accepted the proven practical supremacy of the chronometer and these instruments became standard issue to RN ships. Survey ships, sent out on voyages of exploration, were often issued with many chronometers to ensure improved accuracy in charting coastlines. The *Beagle*, for example, which carried Charles Darwin as naturalist on its celebrated voyage of 1831–36, had 22 chronometers on board.

By this time, the Royal Observatory had adopted a whole new scientific role in testing the accuracy of chronometers, purchasing the good ones and issuing them to Navy ships. For over 100 years this essential testing, which included heating the chronometers in an oven to simulate tropical temperatures, took place in the two rooms below the Great Equatorial Telescope at the Observatory. Getting the very best performance from chronometers became highly scientific, and a very profitable business, and the nineteenth century was a period of intense competition among makers producing these cutting-edge navigational devices. The celebrated maker, Thomas Earnshaw, described them as representing 'the topmost boughs of the tree of mechanism'.

One of the Chronometer Rooms, on the first floor of the Observatory, where the chronometers and deck watches were tested. The ovens can just be seen on the right.

Distributing Time: the Observatory Time-Ball

THE FIRST PUBLIC TIME SIGNAL was broadcast from the roof of Flamsteed House in 1833. The idea of dropping a ball at a predetermined time was the brainchild of Captain Wauchope, RN, and was tested at the Naval College at Portsmouth before Maudslay & Field were commissioned to install the first Greenwich time-ball in that year.

The signal was (and is) given at 1 p.m. because the astronomers would be busy checking the rates of their clocks against the Sun's transit at noon. At 12.55 p.m. the ball is hoisted half-way up the mast – originally a signal for navigators on ships in the Thames and London docks to be ready. At two minutes to the hour the ball is hoisted to the top of the mast and then drops precisely at 1 p.m. From this, sea captains about to sail could check the rate of their marine chronometers, which were in wide use by the 1830s.

The time-ball at Greenwich was originally manually operated. Two assistants wound up the ball and a third pulled a trigger cord to release it exactly on the hour, timed by a regulator. If the ball failed to drop, the fall-back protocol was to lower it slowly and then drop it correctly on the following hour. The final release of the time-ball was controlled electrically from the mid-1800s and the present time-ball is a replacement mechanism that was installed in 1919: this was fully mechanized in the 1960s. Time-balls proliferated in the nineteenth century and became a common feature in ports all around the world. Some of the more remote examples received a signal from the Royal Observatory via submarine cable.

BELOW: **Miniature zinc time-ball**, *c.*1900, from the offices of Gledhill Brook Ltd, Victoria Street, London. It operated until around 1920 by a signal from the Standard Time Company. ZAA0636

OPPOSITE: **The one o'clock time signal** from the roof of Flamsteed House has been a regular occurrence since 1833.

Standardizing Time

AROUND 1800, people were still using local mean solar time, derived from applying the 'equation of time' to sundial readings. However, the second quarter of the nineteenth century saw a rapid expansion in communications that created a real need for standardized time. Principally, it was the railways, the Post Office and telegraphic agencies that were inconvenienced by local time differences. A train passenger from London to Liverpool would have to put his watch back by twelve minutes on arrival. For the traveller it was a minor inconvenience but for the railway companies it became a time-tabling minefield, with all kinds of safety implications.

After becoming seventh Astronomer Royal in 1835, George Biddell Airy repeatedly expressed the opinion that the national observatory was duty-bound to supply Greenwich Mean Time to the nation. Following the Great Exhibition of 1851, he employed clockmaker Charles Shepherd to supply the Observatory with an electri-cal clock system that ran slave dials within the Observatory buildings and also a large public dial by the front gate: this was the first to show Greenwich Time to the public, as it still does. Shepherd's system also transmitted hourly signals to Lewisham railway station and along the wider telegraphic networks.

BELOW: **A gold traveller's watch** made in 1847 by Benjamin Lewis Vulliamy. The gold minute hand can be wound forwards or backwards to represent local mean time while the normal hand showed the owner's 'home' time. ZAA0744

Greenwich Time was in great demand, and was initially sold by private telegraph companies then, after 1870, by the General Post Office. In 1853 an annual subscription to the Greenwich Time Signal in the London area would have cost £15. It was often used creatively to generate interest in shops, some of which incorporated the Greenwich signal into their window displays in order to attract passers-by.

OPPOSITE: **The slave-clock dial** by Shepherd (1852), at the Observatory gate. Controlled by electric signals from the Observatory's master clock it was the first one to show GMT directly to the public. ZAA0533

Time Tested and Restored

T HE ROYAL OBSERVATORY recognized that British naval ships needed Greenwich Time to set their chronometers and, as well as establishing the time-ball signal at Greenwich, time-balls controlled by high-precision 'regulators' were provided at Royal Navy bases around the world. Whenever possible, these regulators were corrected using Greenwich Time sent daily by electric telegraph signal.

It was also in the Chronometer Rooms at the Observatory that the Harrison timekeepers were stored during the nineteenth century. They were

BELOW: **Lt-Cdr Rupert T. Gould, RN** (1890–1948), the remarkable horologist, broadcaster and polymath, who restored the Harrison timekeepers in the 1920s and '30s. He is holding a balance from H2, with the unrestored H3 on the table. F4248

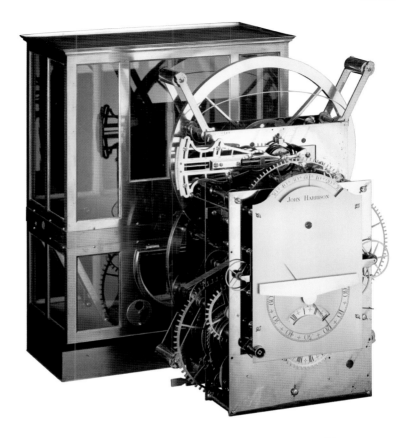

RIGHT: **The restored H3** (1757), with its original protective brass and glass case. The print of Harrison on p. 34 shows it in the case, in a gimbal mount. ZAA0036

kept in poor conditions right by the vents of the gas ovens and became very dilapidated. It was only in the 1920s that they were rescued by Lt-Cdr Rupert Gould, RN, who dedicated the rest of his life to restoring them to their former glory: without his work they may not even have survived at all.

Today the Chronometer Room on the ground floor is partly the National Maritime Museum's horological conservation workshop, and is on public view through the glass of the 'Time for the Navy' showcase. The Museum's horological staff continue the tradition of working on and studying precision timepieces, while also preserving what is the finest collection of its kind anywhere in the world.

Time and Society

TODAY WE TAKE the availability of accurate time for granted. Most people have instant access to highly accurate atomic time in one form or another and there is no need to listen for a radio time-signal on the hour, or telephone the 'speaking clock'. We may wonder how our ancestors coped but, for many, the crowing of the cock, habitual mealtimes and the passage of the Sun were enough to shape their day.

Medieval astronomers, astrologers and travellers some-times carried astrolabes in order to find time. The National Maritime Museum's collection of these is one of the largest in the world and includes masterpieces of mathematical and astronomical engraving. Any two astrolabes can vary enormously in function. The more sophisticated could not only find the time but also the date, make predictions of lunar and solar eclipses and, in the finest examples, contain different plates (tympans) for use in different latitudes. Simpler portable pocket sundials were even more common and the Museum also has an exceptional collection of these.

The sixteenth century saw the beginnings of the mechanical watch. Examples in lavishly decorated enamelled and jewelled cases were soon worn as jewellery or presented as diplomatic gifts; but for more than a century they were very expensive status symbols rather than reliable timekeepers. Improvements to watch-work, such as the balance spring, led to greater accuracy and more humble watches were produced. In the 1700s and early 1800s a single watch would have been the combined work of about fifty individual crafts-men. And so, albeit in the plainest of cases, they could never be cheap. By the late nineteenth century mass-produced, factory-made pocket watches could be bought for as little as a dollar and, (in an 1887 pamphlet), the Waterbury Watch Company boasted that it could produce 1,200 such watches per day.

ABOVE: **A late-nineteenth-century affordable watch** made by the Waterbury Watch Co. ZAA0358

BELOW: **A sixteenth-century European astrolabe** that can be used to determine the time and date but also has a multitude of other functions. The plates on this instrument can be used at 48° and 50° latitude. AST0563

57

Which Meridian?

T HE ROYAL OBSERVATORY, GREENWICH, is the home of the Prime Meridian of the World, Longitude 000° 00' 00". The line originates at the Airy Transit Circle telescope in the Meridian Building and – like all meridians – runs only to the North and South Poles.

The Equator (latitude 000° 00' 00") separates the northern and southern hemispheres and latitude is measured north and south from it. However, there is no equivalent natural line separating the eastern and western hemispheres to use for measuring longitude east and west. People have to choose where the zero line or 'prime meridian' should be. Until 1884 many different meridians were used, including three previous ones at Greenwich. In that year the International Meridian Conference in Washington, DC, agreed that 'the meridian passing through the centre of the [Airy] transit instrument at the Observatory of Greenwich' should be globally adopted for charting; also that the universal day for the world should begin at the moment of mean midnight on the Greenwich meridian.

The Global Positioning System uses a meridian roughly 102.5 m (336 ft) to the east of the Prime Meridian. The coordinates of the central GPS ground-station in the USA were originally calculated from Greenwich, but discrepancies resulted when they were used as the starting point for a new best-fit model of the ellipsoidal shape of the Earth. The GPS meridian is a plane projected from the centre of the Earth's mass into space and so, unlike the Prime Meridian, it cannot be permanently marked as a line on the ground, because the ground is moving with the underlying tectonic plate. The Observatory is moving about 2 cm (¾ in.) closer to the GPS meridian every year.

A view looking south along the Prime Meridian towards the Meridian Building (with the open white door). Airy's transit telescope is housed inside and the Prime Meridian of the World is marked on the paving of the Observatory courtyard. People standing astride the line have one foot in the western hemisphere and the other in the eastern hemisphere.

Telescopes: meridian, zenith, equatorial and altazimuth

T HE CORE OBSERVATIONS at the Royal Observatory – for mapping the stars and the motions of the Sun, Moon and planets – were made with instruments that could only observe north–south. As a star crossed the meridian, astronomers used a mural quadrant or circle to measure its height, and a transit telescope and clock to time the moment of transit. Nevertheless, several other kinds of telescope can be found at the Observatory.

Zenith telescopes point only to the stars straight overhead, which are the least affected by the distortions of atmospheric refraction. Flamsteed experimented unsuccessfully with a zenith telescope set in a deep well. Much more successful was the celebrated zenith sector made by George Graham for James Bradley in 1727. Bradley failed in his aim of observing stellar parallax but made two important discoveries that greatly increased the accuracy of positional astronomy: the aberration of light and the nutation, or slight 'nodding', of the Earth's axis.

The fixed mounts of meridian and zenith instruments allow great precision but are not suitable for wider observations. The mount of an equatorial telescope is aligned to the Earth's axis and allows almost any star to be tracked as the Earth rotates. Over the centuries Greenwich had many equatorial telescopes of all sizes. One of the largest, the 28-inch refracting telescope made in the 1890s, can be seen today in the Great Equatorial Building.

The Observatory also had altazimuth telescopes, used to measure a star's altitude (angular height above the horizon) and azimuth (position in degrees along the horizon). The large altazimuths of George Airy and William Christie are no longer at Greenwich, but it still has the Altazimuth Pavilion, which housed Christie's instrument.

Drawings of Royal Observatory instruments, by John Charnock, c.1785, including Bradley's zenith sector (left), an equatorial telescope (top centre) and a mural quadrant (bottom right). PAF2940

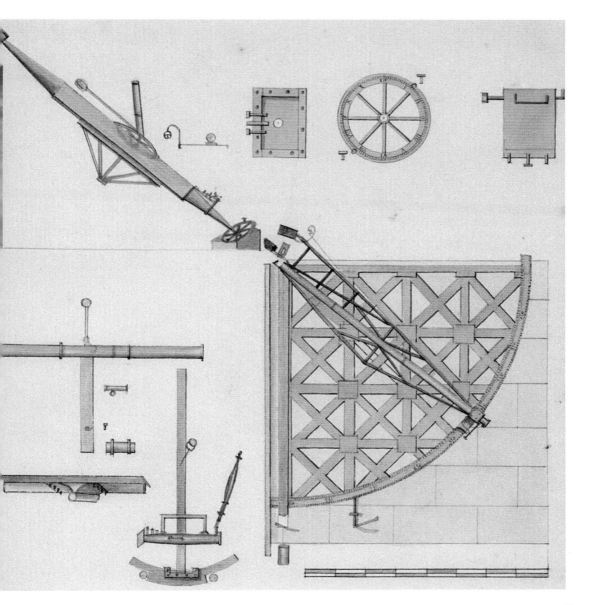

New Ways of Observing

IN THE EARLY 1800s there was a view that astronomy as a science was almost complete, with the theory of gravitation having been perfected over the course of the previous century. William Herschel's famous 40-foot reflecting telescope, the remains of which can be seen at the Royal Observatory today, had also demonstrated the power of these instruments to look ever-deeper into space, but it was unclear what they could do beyond adding to the list of known objects found there.

Two new techniques developed in the nineteenth century began a new chapter for astronomy: photography and spectroscopy. Photography allows detailed measurement of transitory events or large numbers of stars, and the observation of the Sun. Spectroscopy involves the examination of the spectrum of an object's light, which can reveal physical properties such as temperature, mass, motion and chemical composition. In the nineteenth century it allowed many new questions to be asked about the nature of the universe.

At Greenwich, several new instruments and observing programmes were introduced to take advantage of these new techniques. The Observatory helped organize expeditions to observe and photograph solar eclipses and, from the 1870s, took daily photographs of the Sun's surface in order to study the cyclical nature of sun spots. These photographs were taken with photoheliograph telescopes, one of which is today mounted in the Altazimuth Pavilion. Under William Christie, the Observatory also joined an international project, called the *Carte du Ciel*, aiming to produce a photographic map of the stars. Spectroscopy was used to observe the Sun and to reveal the motion of stars through space. Increasingly, such work went beyond the old Greenwich mission of mapping the stars and aiding safe navigation.

E. W. Maunder, the first head of the Observatory's Photographic and Spectroscopic Department, looking into the spectroscope of the 28-inch telescope. B5698

Magnetic and Meteorological Observations

ASTRONOMY WAS NOT THE ONLY SCIENCE pursued at the Observatory. Meteorology – the study of the weather – was another. Indeed, it has long-term astronomical associations, largely because astronomers are inevitably aware of its effects on observing conditions. Clouds, and changes in air pressure and temperature, have significant effects on instruments and the atmosphere, and so thermometer and barometer readings have long been included with astronomical observations.

In the nineteenth century there was increasing interest in developing meteorology as a predictive science by collecting and analysing large amounts of data. The Royal Observatory was well-placed to play an important role, adding to observations collected across Britain and around the world. Given that one aim was improving the safety of shipping, this fitted with the Observatory's original purpose. An important innovation by George Airy, in the 1840s, was the introduction of self-recording instruments. These provided a complete record of changing conditions and reduced the workload of his busy assistants.

At Greenwich, meteorology was closely associated with the observation of geomagnetism. They were united within the Magnetic and Meteorological – or 'Mag & Met' – Department, which was also responsible for taking measurements of variations in the Earth's magnetic field and of atmospheric electricity. This work was undertaken in the Magnet House, later known as the Magnetic Pavilion, a building constructed of materials such as wood, with brass nails, that would not interfere with the magnetic and electrical instruments.

One of the most significant results of the Observatory's magnetic observations was a conclusive demonstration by E. Walter Maunder, head of the Photographic and Spectroscopic Department, of the relationship between the sunspot cycle and magnetic storms on Earth.

The Observatory in the late nineteenth century, taken from the south, showing the wooden, cruciform Magnet House and several small huts and shelters for meteorological instruments. The brick building on the right held the library. 3100

19th-century Expansion

THE PIECEMEAL EXPANSION of the Royal Observatory's site reveals much about the history of the institution and astronomy: the growth of the staff, the range of work undertaken, the development of new kinds of astronomy, and the increasing willingness of governments to support scientific services and, later, research. Money was always limited and directed to the most practical and useful work of the Observatory. Constraints were also created by the site's location: it could not be expanded north or west, because of the hill, and being within the Royal Park meant that every inch of new land added had to be approved by Royal Warrant.

In the 1830s the Observatory site was almost doubled in order to accommodate a new Magnet House, which required a degree of isolation from other buildings. The 1850s saw the arrival of the Great Equatorial Building (to the east of what is today called the Meridian Building), to hold George Airy's 12.8-inch equatorial telescope beneath a drum-shaped dome. In the 1890s this was replaced by William Christie's 28-inch telescope, a larger instrument accommodated on the same mount but within a new, onion-shaped dome.

Significant building work took place in the 1890s under Christie, who helped design the Altazimuth Pavilion and New Physical Observatory. The latter, soon known simply as the South Building, originally contained some

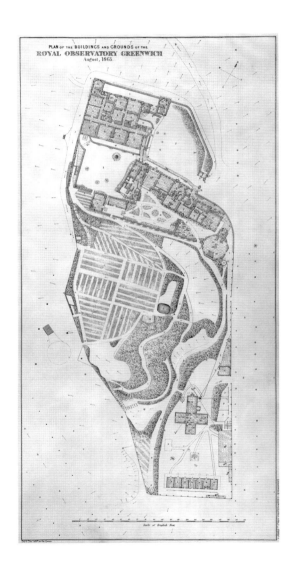

OPPOSITE: **Site plan** of the Observatory in 1862, from an appendix to that year's published *Greenwich Observations*.

ABOVE: **The New Physical Observatory**, or South Building, under construction in the 1890s. In the right foreground are a number of meteorological instruments in wooden shelters. B1006-10

large equatorial telescopes and offices for the astronomers, assistants and (human) computers, as well as stores, records, workshops and darkrooms. It provided much-needed space but was designed to be a prominent, coherent and attractive building in keeping with the importance of a national institution. Its terracotta decoration includes a pantheon of names, listing astronomers and instrument makers significant to the Observatory's history.

Into the 20th Century

IN 1899, the Observatory enclosed some land within Greenwich Park to rehouse the magnetic instruments, by then suffering interference from the South Building. By the 1930s several other instruments were placed there, including the 36-inch Yapp reflecting telescope. This, and other telescopes used at Greenwich, can be seen today at the Observatory Science Centre at Herstmonceux in Sussex, where the institution moved in the 1950s. At that time, many of the utilitarian later buildings at Greenwich were also demolished.

The need to move away from Greenwich first became apparent in the late nineteenth century. Increasingly, there were problems with smoke and light pollution, as both London and its Thames-side industry expanded. New train lines also caused problems, first with vibrations and then, after the electrification of the Southern Railway in 1923, with serious interference to magnetic observations. This meant the work had to be moved to a new site at Abinger in Surrey.

LEFT: **Bomb damage** to the Observatory in the Second World War, during which essential work and expensive telescope lenses were moved away from Greenwich.

ABOVE: **The truncated bronze cone** covering the planetarium dome. Its form and orientation reflect the local meridian and latitude. Behind is the South Building, now home to the Astronomy Galleries and learning centre.

Conditions continued to deteriorate and it fell to Harold Spencer Jones to plan a move. It was delayed by the Second World War but in the 1940s and 1950s the various departments were resettled at Herstmonceux Castle as the 'Royal Greenwich Observatory'. Under this title it moved again in 1990, to Cambridge, and was finally closed in 1998.

From 1953 the old Greenwich site became part of the National Maritime Museum. Flamsteed House opened to the public in 1960 and, after renovations, the other surviving buildings followed suit by 1967. Since then the buildings and displays have been redeveloped several times. Today they explain the history of the Observatory, the search for longitude, and the role of Greenwich Mean Time. Since 2007 the new Astronomy Galleries and the Peter Harrison Planetarium have aimed to inspire visitors with modern discoveries in astronomy and space exploration.

Evolving Observatories

IN THE TWENTIETH CENTURY new observatories began to be built on the tops of mountains, high above the clouds and away from the increasing light pollution of towns and cities. The dark skies and excellent viewing conditions at these remote sites allowed telescopes to see further into deep space than ever before, showing a wealth of new detail in familiar objects and revealing whole new types of astronomical phenomena.

At the same time, evolving technology began to open new windows onto the universe, through telescopes designed to detect radiation beyond the visible spectrum of light. This allowed astronomers to observe things previously unseen using gamma rays, X-rays, ultraviolet and infrared radiation, microwave and radio emissions.

The space age also brought exciting new opportunities for scientists, as unmanned robotic probes were sent out to explore the solar system. Space-craft have now visited all eight of the planets and several moons, asteroids and comets, sending back spectacular close-up images. For the first time we can see these distant worlds as real places, with their own history, weather and geology. People have also ventured into space and in 1969 the crew of *Apollo 11* became the first humans to set foot on another world when they landed on the Moon.

Observatories continue to evolve. By launching instruments like the Hubble Space Telescope into orbit, astronomers avoid the problems of cloud cover and atmospheric blurring which affect telescopes on Earth. Meanwhile, a new generation of giant telescopes is being planned, with mirrors up to tens of metres across that can collect the light from extremely faint and distant objects. There is no doubt that these observatories of the future will continue to challenge our understanding of the universe and our place within it.

The design for the proposed European Extremely Large Telescope. The telescope will have a mirror 40 metres (132 feet) in diameter and its protective dome will rival that of St Paul's cathedral in scale.

Modern Astronomy

WITH IMPROVEMENTS in telescope technology, the twentieth century saw huge advances in the fields of astronomy, astrophysics and cosmology. Our understanding of the cosmos was transformed and the universe came to be seen as an even vaster and more complex place than the first Astronomer Royal at Greenwich could ever have imagined.

New discoveries came thick and fast. In the 1920s Edwin Hubble found that our own Milky Way galaxy is just one among billions of others. Further observations showed that space itself is expanding: not only is the universe vaster than anyone had guessed, it is also getting bigger all the time. Advances in physics allowed scientists to explain longstanding problems, such as the source of energy which powers the Sun and the other stars. Meanwhile, unexpected discoveries like quasars, pulsars and dark matter required new theories to explain them.

At the close of the twentieth century our picture of the universe was changed again by the discovery that, rather than gradually slowing, its expansion is actually getting faster, propelled by a mysterious quantity called 'dark energy'. Astronomy now gives us perhaps the most accurate picture of the universe that we have ever had: it is 13.7 thousand million years old and made up of 73 per cent dark energy and 23 per cent dark matter, with the 'ordinary matter' which makes up the visible cosmos of stars, planets and people contributing only 4 per cent of the total.

Today, still early in the twenty-first century, exciting progress is being made on many of the questions which have taxed astronomers' minds for millennia: how did the universe begin? Where did life come from? Are we alone? In 1995 the first planet orbiting a star other than our own sun was discovered around the star 51 Pegasi. Now we know of hundreds of stars with their own planetary systems and the hunt is on for planets which closely resemble the Earth.

The future is hard to predict and it may be that some unexpected new discovery will, once again, challenge everything we thought we knew about the universe. What is certain is that the next century of astronomy will be just as exciting as the last.

OPPOSITE: **'The Pillars of Creation'**. Columns of dust and gas in the Eagle nebula, imaged by the Hubble Space Telescope. They are part of a stellar nursery in which new stars are being formed. (The black area, top right, was not imaged by the telescope.)

OVERLEAF: **Old and new**: (left) the Observatory's Altazimuth Pavilion, 1899, with its Halley's Comet wind-vane, and the dome covering the 28-inch telescope of 1893 behind; (right) the Hubble Space Telescope, placed in orbit 559 km (347 miles) above the Earth in 1990, by the shuttle *Discovery*.

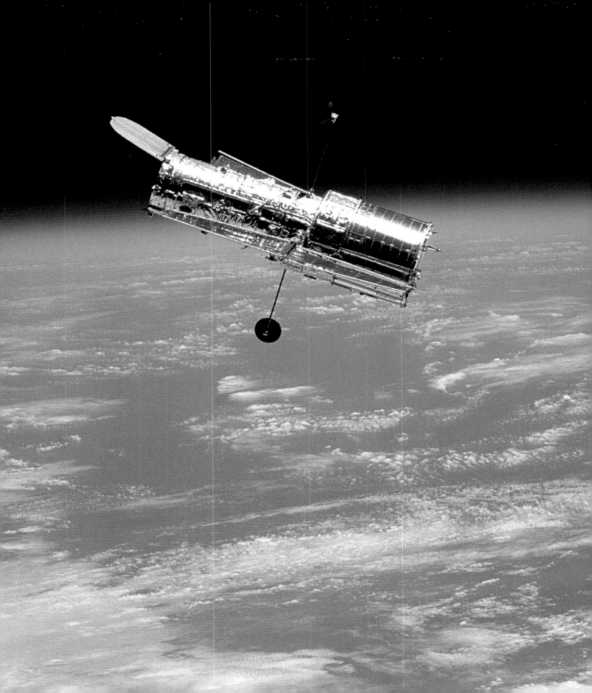

New Directions at Greenwich

THE FOCUS OF ASTRONOMY RESEARCH moved away from observatories like Greenwich long ago, but the historic buildings, instruments and documents here continue to bring the ongoing story of the subject to visitors from around the world.

As astronomers continue to ask challenging new questions about the universe, their discoveries are reflected in the Royal Observatory's Weller Galleries of Astronomy and in the varied programme of the Peter Harrison Planetarium. Here, topics like the Big Bang, black holes, supernovae, extra-solar planets and dark matter are presented and explained, as the latest chapters in astronomy's long story.

The internet has enabled the Royal Observatory to take part in cutting-edge astronomical projects once again. The Observatory's 'Solar Stormwatch' website invites members of the public to become 'citizen scientists', helping researchers to analyse satellite images of the Sun and improve our understanding of our nearest star and its effects on the Earth. Another online project is the Observatory's Astronomy Photographer of the Year competition. This attracts hundreds of entries from both amateur and professional photographers around the world, who submit awe-inspiring images of the night sky.

The Royal Observatory also contributes to modern astronomy through its extensive programme of workshops and activities for schools. By training and inspiring the next generation of scientists it is actively helping to ensure that the future of astronomy will be as exhilarating and surprising as its past.

The Peter Harrison Planetarium has an ever-changing programme. Here images of the classical constellations wheel across the inner surface of the dome during one of the regular shows.

Find Out More

Collections Online: collections.rmg.co.uk

Our Collections Online website includes descriptions and images of objects in the astronomy, maps and charts, horology and navigation collections. Many of these were historically associated with the Royal Observatory.

The Library and Archive: rmg.co.uk/researchers/

Over two million items are held in the National Maritime Museum's new Caird Library, which was opened in 2011. These include books, manuscripts, ephemera, prints, drawings, charts, maps and atlases, which can be found and pre-ordered using the online catalogue. As well as modern works relating to the Observatory's themes, the Library holds an important collection of rare books. Among these is the Airy Collection, which was inherited from the Observatory and includes many key sixteenth- to nineteenth-century works. The archives of the Observatory itself are held in the Manuscripts Department of Cambridge University Library.

Learning at the Royal Observatory, Greenwich

A year-round programme of activities for all ages explores the collections, site and themes of the Observatory. There are study courses, including GCSE Astronomy, opportunities for observation with the large 28-inch refracting telescope, and a wide range of conferences, lectures, workshops, performances and tours focusing on history and modern science.

ABOVE: **The wind vane** over the Observatory's South Building. It represents Henry VIII's flagship, *Henri Grace à Dieu*, or 'Great Harry'.

Further Reading

The website includes a range of resources for those interested in the history of the Observatory and modern or historical astronomy, cartography, navigation and timekeeping. Two key books on the history of the Observatory are: Derek Howse, *Greenwich Time and Longitude* (Philip Wilson, 2003) and Eric Forbes, A. J. Meadows and Derek Howse, *Greenwich Observatory* (3 vols, Taylor & Francis, 1975).

OPPOSITE: **Looking at Halley's Comet**, by John James Chalon. A watercolour sketch showing excited adults and children observing the comet's return in 1835 through a telescope set up in a village street. PAJ1974

This edition (amended second printing) published on behalf of
Royal Museums Greenwich by NMM Enterprises Ltd, 2012.
All text and images © National Maritime Museum, Greenwich, UK, 2012
with the exception of: p. 14, © The Royal Society, London (ref. P0151);
p. 49, © BT Heritage (ref. E6008); p. 68, by kind permission of the Science
and Technology Facilities Council and the Syndics of Cambridge
University Library (ref. RGO10714); p. 70, Swinburne Astronomy
Productions/ESO; p. 73, NASA, ESA, STScI, J. Hester and P. Scowen
(Arizona State University) [ref. hs-1995-4-a]; p. 75, NASA (GPN-2000-001064)

National Maritime Museum
Royal Museums Greenwich
London SE10 9NF
www.rmg.co.uk

ISBN: 978 1 906367 51 0

With thanks to the Royal Museums Greenwich staff authors:
Jonathan Betts, Richard Dunn, Rebekah Higgitt,
Gillian Hutchinson, Marek Kukula and Rory McEvoy

Project managed by Lara Maiklem and Diana Christou
Edited by Pieter van der Merwe
Designed by Nigel Soper
Cover design by Shaun Campbell
Photography by Tina Warner and David Westwood
Production management by Geoff Barlow

Printed in the UK by Belmont Press

10   9   8   7   6   5   4   3   2   1

OPPOSITE: **Longitude 0°**
is marked at night by
the laser beam shining
northwards from above
the Observatory's Airy
Transit Circle.

FRONT COVER: **Northern
hemisphere constellations**
from an atlas engraving
by Carolo Allard, 1700.
G200:1/1A-B